TEACHER RESOURCE GUIDE

First published SADDLEBACK PUBLISHING, INC.
Three Watson Irvine, CA 92618–2767
Published under licence 2009 by R.I.C. PUBLICATIONS® PTY LTD

Distributed by:

Australasia
R.I.C. Publications®, PO Box 332, Greenwood 6924, Western Australia:
www.ricpublications.com.au

UK/Republic of Ireland
Prim-Ed Publishing, Bosheen, New Ross, County Wexford, Republic of Ireland
www.prim-ed.com

Japan, Korea and Taiwan
R.I.C. Publications, 5th Floor, Gotanda Mikado Building,
2–5–8 Hiratsuka, Shinagawa–Ku Tokyo, Japan 142–0051:
www.ricpublications.com

Malaysia and Brunei
Penerbitan B.R.I.C. Sdn. Bhd.
S/Lot 31, Block 217 KNLD, Batu Kawa Light Industrial Park, MJC.
Jalan Batu Kawa, 93250, Kuching, Sarawak, Malaysia.
www.ricpublications.com.au

©2008 Saddleback Publishing Inc. All rights reserved.
This edition ©Prim-Ed Publishing 2010

PR–6726

ISBN   978-1-84654-251-0

Contents

Name .... Date ....

Word parts

The word *anitmicrobial* comes from the word parts *anti* (meaning 'against') and *microbial* (meaning 'a tiny bacteria'). In other words, an antimicrobial fights against small germs.

Directions: Combine the word parts in the box to create words from the book. Apply the explanations of the word parts to write your own definition for each word. Use the book or a dictionary if needed. You can use each word part more than once.

> *anti* – against
> *auto* – self
> *carbo* – carbon
> *fungal* – anything related to fungus
> *hydro* or *hydrate* – water
> *litho* – stone
> *phyte* – plant growth
> *troph* – nutrition or nourishment

_____

_____

_____

_____

_____

_____

Related words

Many of the word parts you used in the activity above also appear in other words; e.g.

anti-aircraft   lithograph.

Directions: List other words you know that use word parts from the box above.

_____

_____

_____

_____

Name .... Date ....

Label groups

What do these words have in common?

eucalyptus   **banksia**   **pine**

They are all species of evergreen trees.

Directions: Write a label for each group of words to tell what the words or phrases have in common. Add another word or phrase to each list.

1. Label: _____

    carbon dioxide   *light*   *water*   _____

2. Label: _____

    sago   *date*   *raffia*   _____

3. Label: _____

    temperate rainforest   *boreal*   *subtropical*   _____

4. Label: _____

    wind   *falling seeds*   *animals*   _____

5. Label: _____

    stem   *leaf*   *root*   _____

6. Label: _____

    antifungal compounds   *thorns*   *fire-resistant bark*   _____

Do-it-yourself groupings

Directions: Create your own category of plant-related words or phrases from the book. Write a label, then list as many words as possible that go together to make a group.

_____

_____

_____

_____

_____

Name .... Date ....

Create a diagram

The book *Factoscope*: *Plants* has many diagrams. You can use them as examples to create your own diagram about a topic from the book.

Directions: Create a diagram or chart to better display a section of the information given in the text. Choose from one of the ideas below or think of one of your own. Do more research, if needed. Consider including in your diagram: a title, a key, labels, colours, illustrations etc.

> • **The process of seed dispersal**
> • **The cycle of plant growth from seed to root to flowering plant**
> • **World map showing the types of plants that grow in each region**
> • **Chart comparing major types of plants to each other, such as grasses, trees and aquatic plants**

Name .... Date ....

Grow-your-own experiment

What happens to a plant that doesn't receive any light, that isn't rooted in soil, that isn't watered every day? Carry out this experiment and find out.

Directions: Get six healthy plant cuttings, all taken from the same plant. All should be about the same size and colour. Find out how to take care of them. Plant each cutting in its own container and follow the directions below. Use the 'Plant condition chart' on the next page to record your observations. Once the experiment is finished, write a paragraph or two about what you learned on a separate sheet of paper.

- Label one plant 'Control'. This is the plant you will treat correctly. That means that you water it as advised, and place it where it will receive the proper amount of light and be in the correct temperature range.

- Label one plant 'Dark' and put it somewhere where it receives no light at all (perhaps in a cupboard or under a large piece of furniture). Do remember to water it as often as you water the Control plant. Just don't forget where you placed or put it anywhere near where a pet can get to it!

- Label one plant 'Dry' and put it where it will get the proper amount of light. But don't water it.

- Label one plant 'Rocks' and plant it in pebbles or rocks instead of soil. Water it correctly and place it next to the Control plant.

- Depending on the time of year and the conditions where you live, label a plant either 'Hot' or 'Cold' and place it outside or close to a heating or air conditioning vent. Make sure it gets the proper amount of water and light. You may want to put it next to the Control plant during the day, then move it after the sun goes down.

- Label one plant 'Water' and give this plant twice as much water as is recommended. Place this plant next to the Control.

- If you think of another variable you would like to try, make sure to label your plant and be consistent with what you do.

Name .... Date ....

Plant condition chart

Directions: Complete the chart as you conduct your plant condition experiment.

	What you predict will happen	Observe: How the plants look after one week	Observe: How the plants look after two weeks	Observe: How the plants look after three weeks
Control				
Dark				
Dry				
Rocks				
Hot/Cold				
Water				

Name .... Date ....

Everyday inventory

desk   ⟶   wood   ⟶   tree

Much of your desk may come from wood, which comes from a tree. What else around your house comes from plants?

Directions: Create more diagrams to show what objects around your house are made from plants or plant products.

1. _____ ⟶ _____ ⟶ _____

2. _____ ⟶ _____ ⟶ _____

3. _____ ⟶ _____ ⟶ _____

4. _____ ⟶ _____ ⟶ _____

5. _____ ⟶ _____ ⟶ _____

6. _____ ⟶ _____ ⟶ _____

7. _____ ⟶ _____ ⟶ _____

8. _____ ⟶ _____ ⟶ _____

9. _____ ⟶ _____ ⟶ _____

10. _____ ⟶ _____ ⟶ _____

Name .... Date ....

Garden classification

What kinds of plants do you *see* every day? Go into your garden or neighbourhood park and look.

Directions: Use the book *Factoscope: Plants* as a guide. Take it with you as you look around your garden or the park. Add to each list below the names of plants you observe. Use the most specific name as possible for each plant. An outside source such as a gardening book, the Internet or a gardener may be helpful. Three of the lists are labelled for you. Create three other lists based on the plants you observe. Use such labels as *mosses, aquatic, roses, deciduous trees.*

grasses	shrubs	weeds

Name .... Date ....

Scavenger hunt

Use the index of *Factoscope*: *Plants* and a stopwatch to test your hunting skills.

Directions: Go it alone or team up with a partner and compete against another pair to see who can find the answers to these questions first. Keep track of your time.

1. If a root system is not adventitious, what is it most likely to be?

    _____

2. What are spores?_____

3. List five places, besides soil, where mosses grow. _____

    _____

4. Find the definitions for the words *perennial* and *biennial*. What do you think the word

    part *-ennial* means? _____

    _____

5. In what three categories might you put bonsai?

    _____

    _____

6. Thallose plants usually lack leaves and stems. What is another form of the word *thallose*?

    _____

    _____

7. Where might you expect to find cycads? _____

    _____

8. The word part *chloro* means 'green'. In which two words listed in the index does it

    appear? _____

    _____

9. What clues in the words *dicots* and *monocots* can help you tell the flowers apart?

    _____

    _____

10. Name a cycad palm that is not necessarily a palm. _____

Name .... Date ....

Cloze

What word best completes the thought?

Directions: Choose a word from the box to fill in each blank to have the paragraph make sense. Hint: Not all words will be used.

adapt	chlorophyll	colours
endangered	extinct	leaves
palo	verde	phloem
photosynthesis	pollinate	reproduce
saguaro cactus	stems	varieties

Plants come in countless _____, growing all over the Earth. But some features are shared by most plants. For example, it's the green colouring in plants, called _____, that helps with photosynthesis. Most plants photosynthesise through their _____—but not all. One hot desert tree, the _____ _____, actually has green bark because it often drops its leaves to combat water loss. Then the tree still has what it needs for _____. To continue the species, plants need to _____, which involves fruit, flowers, seeds and pollen. When a plant species begins to disappear in great numbers, and may soon cease to exist, the plant is said to be _____.

 Prim-Ed Publishing®

Name .... Date ....

Write definitions

Echinoderm means 'prickly or spiny skinned'. Echinoderms are marine animals, such as starfish and sea urchins.

Directions: Read each sentence and write your own definition for the underlined word or phrase.

1. People believe that animals have an <u>internal clock</u> that wakes them from their hibernation period.

   _____

   _____

2. Many desert animals are <u>nocturnal</u>, so they avoid the hot rays of the sun.

   _____

   _____

3. Scavengers eat <u>carrion</u>, cleaning the world of organic trash.

   _____

   _____

4. Some lemurs are completely <u>arboreal</u>, while others spend their time both in trees and on land.

   _____

   _____

5. Snakes are not the only animals that can be <u>venomous</u>—many other species have clever ways to inject enemies with a toxin too.

   _____

   _____

6. Frogs <u>inhabit</u> moist and warm areas.

   _____

   _____

Name .... Date ....

Like and unlike

The words *backbone* and *vertebrae* are synonyms. Their meanings are similar, but not exactly the same. *Backbone* means 'spine' and *vertebra* means 'bone of the spine'.

Directions: Match the animal word in the left column with a related word from the right column. For each pair of words, write a sentence telling how the meanings of the words are similar or different.

_____	1. migrate	a.	Arctic
_____	2. hibernate	b.	shell
_____	3. exoskeleton	c.	move
_____	4. polar	d.	genus
_____	5. species	e.	aestivate

1. _____

_____

2. _____

_____

3. _____

_____

4. _____

_____

5. _____

_____

Synonym or antonym

Nocturnal means 'night-time'; *diurnal* means 'daytime'. They are antonyms.

Directions: Write S if the pair of words are synonyms, A if they are antonyms.

_____	1. poison: venom	_____	4. gigantic: tiny
_____	2. gnaw: chew	_____	5. breathes: respirates
_____	3. rare: common	_____	6. flourishing: endangered

Name .... Date ....

Venn diagram

Look at the pairs of animals below. Think about how they compare and contrast.

frogs and toads   **turtles and tortoises**   **crocodiles and alligators**

Directions: Circle one of the pairs of animals. Create a Venn diagram to compare and contrast them. Write the facts that are different about each animal in its own oval. Write the facts that are similar in the area the two ovals share.

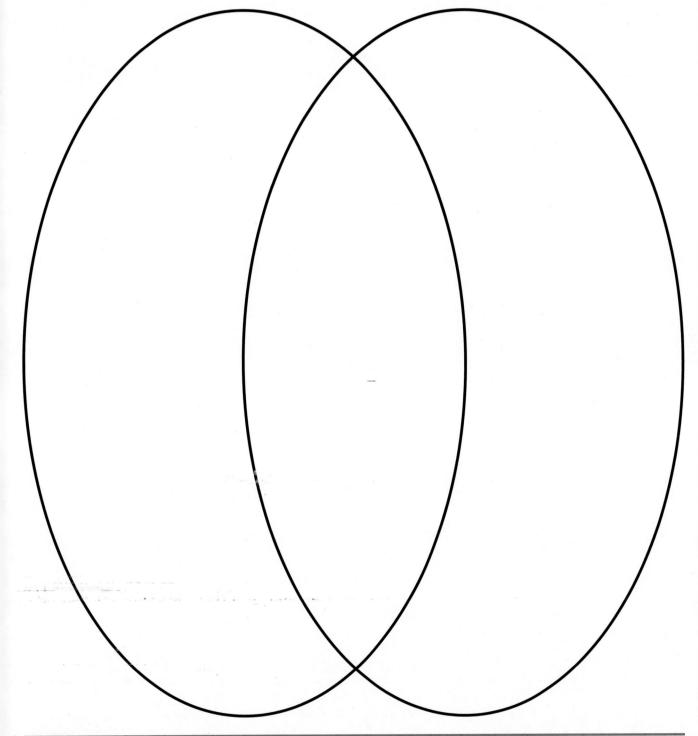

Name .... Date ....

Classifications

Tarantulas fit all the following classifications: arachnid, invertebrate, carnivore, insectivore, hot desert and tropical rainforest dweller, and oviparous (egg-laying).

Directions: List as many classifications as possible for each animal. For items 7 and 8, list classifications for animals that *you* find interesting.

1. blue-ringed octopus _____

   _____

   _____

2. platypus _____

   _____

   _____

3. honey bee _____

   _____

   _____

4. bear _____

   _____

   _____

5. penguin _____

   _____

   _____

6. squirrel _____

   _____

   _____

7. _____

   _____

   _____

8. _____

   _____

Name .... Date ....

Your local habitat

Lobsters live in freshwater habitats. Do you live near a freshwater pond or lake? If so, are there any lobsters living there? What else lives in your area? Think about fish, insects, birds and other animals you have observed.

Directions: Make a list of the animals that live within your area. For each animal, describe its environment (underground, arboreal, saltwater etc.). Compare your list with those of your classmates.

Animal	Environment	Animal	Environment
1.		8.	
2.		9.	
3.		10.	
4.		11.	
5.		12.	
6.		13.	
7.		14.	

Name .... Date ....

Habitat observations

Directions: Answer these questions about the habitat activity you completed on the previous worksheet.

1. What kind of habitat do you live in or near? _____

   _____

   _____

2. What types of animals live near you? _____

   _____

   _____

3. Did you discover any animals living near you that you had never noticed before? If so,

   which ones? _____

   _____

   _____

4. Which animals make your living environment a better place? Explain your choices.

   _____

   _____

5. Which animals make your living environment a more dangerous or dirtier place?

   _____

   _____

6. What animal would you like to live closer to? Why do you think this animal is not part

   of your local habitat? _____

   _____

   _____

7. Are there migratory animals in your area? Describe their pattern of coming and going.

   _____

   _____

   _____

Name .... Date ....

Choose a project

Directions: Read the following options. Choose one project to complete on the following page.

Project 1: *Helping endangered animals*

Research what you, as a pupil, can do to help the cause of endangered animals. Find out about organisations whose missions include helping endangered species. Some organisations are concerned with just one species, while some work to solve problems for all endangered animals. Write a one-page summary of what a person your age can do to help prevent animal extinction.

Project 2: *Mapping habitats*

Draw a map of your area that shows the various habitats and types of animals living in each habitat. Show natural features of the landscape on your map such as streams and rivers, lakes, mountains, forests and farmland. Be sure to include a key that identifies the habitats, their characteristics and the animals that inhabit them.

Project 3: *A day in the life*

Choose an animal to follow for a day or part of a day. Keep your distance so you don't scare the animal away. Take notes on what the animal does, eats, where it goes and what it interacts with. After you make your observations, create a day-in-the-life account of that animal. Try to make it as interesting as possible and provide your readers with a better understanding of this animal. For example, your account may be about a magpie, written from the bird's point of view.

Project 4: *Pet training guide*

Do you have experience in training a dog, a horse or a bird? Write a guide for someone who is training a pet. Keep it simple. Begin by describing the characteristics and behaviour of the pet you have chosen. Challenge your reader to teach basic commands and tricks that the pet can master. Explain how to use food treats and praise as a reward. Make sure your instructions are clear and in order.

Name ....   Date ....

Scavenger hunt

Use the index of *Factoscope: Animal world* and a stopwatch to test your hunting skills.

Directions: Go it alone or team up with a partner and compete against another pair to see who can find the answers to these questions first. Keep track of your time.

1. Besides many common hot desert animals, what other animal is identified in the book as nocturnal? _____

   _____

2. What do carrion bugs and sharks have in common? _____

   _____

3. What is the largest land predator? _____

   _____

4. In what way is a cuttlefish like a chameleon? _____

   _____

5. Name two animals that have blubber. _____

   _____

6. What is distinctive about a terrapin? _____

   _____

7. Name two animals from the tropics that are not land animals.

   _____

8. To which group of animals do antelopes belong? _____

   _____

9. What do some animals do during cold winters if they don't hibernate?

   _____

   _____

10. What animal is found wild only on the islands of Borneo and Sumatra?

   _____

   _____

Name .... Date ....

Cloze

What word best completes the thought?

Directions: Choose a word from the box to fill in each blank to have the paragraph make sense. Hint: Not all words will be used.

animals	breathe
characteristics	environment
fish	grow
habitat	invertebrates
oxygen	vertebrate
spine	worms

Animals have four _____ that set them apart from other living things. They can move, breathe, _____ and reproduce. Many other living things can do some of these, but not all of them. All marine animals must _____, they just do it differently than land animals. Just like mammals, fish need _____. So they take in water through their mouths and pass it over their gills. The gills act like lungs, taking the oxygen the body needs. Obviously, each animal is suited to its surroundings, which is why it lives in a particular _____. The largest group of animals in the sea, air and on land is _____. The animals in this category have no _____. Examples are insects, coral, starfish, squid, arachnid and _____.

Name .... Date ....

Prior knowledge

You probably already know more about Earth than you realise. Do this activity before you read *Factoscope: Earth* to find out what you do—and don't—already know.

Directions: Put a tick next to the words you know have something to do with Earth, its features or the study of Earth. Circle words that are unfamiliar to you or that do not seem to have anything to do with the study of Earth. Look for these words as you read the book.

cartographers	equator
insectivores	tectonic plates
zooplankton	solar radiation
geodesy	seismic scale
troglobite	permafrost
humus	watershed

Word parts

The word *prehistoric* means 'before recorded history', while the word *predict* means 'to tell before it happens'. The word part *pre* means 'before'.

Directions: Study each pair of words and their definitions. Then underline the word part they have in common and write your own definition of the word part.

1. **photosynthesis** *(pho/to/syn/the/sis)*: the process by which plants use light to make energy

   photophore *(pho/to/phore)*: an organ of certain marine animals that produces light

   _____

   _____

2. **extrusive** *(ex/tru/sive)*: tending to push out or come out of something

   exoskeleton *(ex/o/skel/e/ton)*: a hard covering on the outside of an animal's body

   _____

   _____

3. **semiaquatic** *(sem/i/a/quat/ic)*: living in and close to water, but not entirely aquatic

   semiarid *(sem/i/ar/id)*: having little rainfall, but not completely arid

   _____

   _____

Name .... Date ....

Word scramble

If you unscramble the phrase *I CRUSH NEAR*, you can spell the word *hurricanes*.

Directions: Look at the phrase and read the hint. Then unscramble the phrase to form an Earth-related vocabulary word. Look for words in the book for help.

1. **HEART QUAKE** *Hint:* sudden vibrations

   _____

2. **OCEAN TIPI TRIP** *Hint:* water that falls to Earth's surface from clouds

   _____

3. **SUB MAT RUTS** *Hint:* one of the layers of surface soil

   _____

4. **UNITED LOGS** *Hint:* vertical lines drawn on world maps, also used to separate the time zones

   _____

5. **LIME CAT** *Hint:* average weather pattern in an area over a period of years

   _____

6. **MAN SUIT** *Hint:* huge tidal wave on the surface of the ocean

   _____

7. **ORIENT UP** *Hint:* when molten rock, volcanic ash and steam rushes out of the Earth's surface

   _____

8. **TINY SMEARED** *Hint:* rock formed from loose rock particles, and plant and animal materials that have built up

   _____

9. **NANCE FLIT DIRT TON** *Hint:* theory about moving continents

   _____

10. **CHOP MEAT RIM** *Hint:* rock formed from other rock broken down by high temperatures

   _____

Name .... Date ....

Cause and effect

Causes and effects are related. An event can be both a cause and an effect. For example, you may flip through some playing cards and get a paper cut on your finger. Then your finger may start to bleed a bit. The paper cut is both the effect of flipping through the playing cards and the cause of your finger bleeding.

Directions: Sort the words and phrases below by writing a cause in the left column and its related effect in the right column. Hint: Some will belong in both columns.

earthquake	time of day varies around the globe
Earth rotates relative to the sun	flood
hot lava cools	igneous rock forms
precipitation falls in some form	rivers flow
tectonic plates move	tsunami
valleys form	water condenses in the clouds

Cause	Effect
1.	1.
2.	2.
3.	3.
4.	4.
5.	5.
6.	6.
7.	7.

Explain

Directions: Choose a related cause and effect from above and explain how the cause creates the effect.

_____

_____

_____

Name .... Date ....

Create a diagram

The book *Factoscope: Earth* has many diagrams. You can use them as examples to create your own diagram about a topic from the book.

Directions: Create a diagram or chart to better display a section of the information given in the text. Choose from one of the ideas below or think of one of your own. Do more research, if needed. Consider including these features in your diagram: a title, a key, labels, colours, illustrations etc.

- **soil layers** *(see page 14)*
- **clouds** *(see page 18)*
- **Ocean zones and their plants and animals** *(see page 27)*
- **Types of mountains** *(see page 35)*
- **How rocks are formed** *(see pages 48–51)*
- **Renewable and non-renewable resources** *(see page 62)*

Name .... Date ....

Local features project

The longest river on Earth is the Nile. Have you ever seen it? What is the longest river closest to you and have you ever seen it?

Directions: Use a map, encyclopedia or the Internet to find the answers to these questions.

1. What is the longest river in or close to, your country? _____

    _____

2. What is the longest river or stream you have ever seen? Where is it located?

    _____

    _____

3. The equator is 0° latitude. Greenwich Mean Time (GMT) starts at 0° longitude. What is the latitude and longitude of your city or town? What time zone do you live in?

    _____

    _____

4. Natural disasters occur frequently around the world. Where and when was a recent

    natural disaster? _____

    _____

5. Exactly how far are you from an ocean? Which ocean are you closest to?

    _____

    _____

6. What types of forests are found in your area? Any?

    _____

7. Have you ever seen a waterfall? What type and where was it? _____

    _____

8. Where is the closest hot desert? Was your area ever covered by desert?

    _____

    _____

Name .... Date ....

Natural wonders

Factoscope: Earth mentions the Grand Canyon, which is one of the Seven Wonders of Natural World. Complete this project to learn about all the seven wonders.

Directions: Read the brief description of each natural wonder: Look in the book, then another source for more information about it. Find it on a map.

Grand Canyon, USA – Carved by wind and the Colorado River, this awesome gorge is 29 kilometres wide in places and 1.83 kilometres deep. The national park it is located in is almost 5000 square kilometres in area.

Great Barrier Reef, off the north-east coast of Australia – The largest coral reef in the world stretches over 2000 kilometres. Almost one-third of the world's coral is there! Besides coral, millions of other plants and animals live in and around it.

aurora borealis, Northern Hemisphere – Highly charged solar energy is especially attracted to the poles. As that energy reaches the atmosphere, it reacts with gases and gives off a colourful light display.

Victoria Falls, between Zambia and Zimbabwe – Although the waterfall is neither the tallest nor the widest, it is the largest sheet of falling water in the world. Its spray can be seen above from kilometres away, earning its local name Mosi-oa-Tunya, which means, 'the smoke that thunders'.

Paricutin Volcano, Mexico – This volcano exploded out of a cornfield almost overnight. It caused lightning and buried one town in lava. It almost covered a neighbouring town 16 kilometres away within two years.

Mount Everest, between Nepal and Tibet, China – Everest is the highest mountain on Earth. The mountain is so tall that it is always covered by snow and ice. Only the most expert climbers attempt to climb it, and even they must obtain a costly permit to do so.

The harbour at Rio de Janeiro, Brazil – The harbour is surrounded by steep mountains, beaches and the teeming city of Rio de Janeiro. Many islands dot the harbour itself. It is an interesting mix of natural beauty and modern living.

Name .... Date ....

Map the Seven Wonders

Directions: Sketch a map of the world and, using the previous work sheet, label each natural wonder.

Your thoughts

Directions: Write a sentence or two to answer each question.

1. Which of the Seven Natural Wonders do you think deserves the title 'Best of the best'?

   _____

   _____

2. Is there another natural wonder you would add to the list? Which would you replace?

   _____

   _____

Name .... Date ....

Scavenger hunt

Use the index of *Factoscope: Earth* and a stopwatch to test your hunting skills.

Directions: Go it alone or team up with a partner and compete against another pair to see who can find the answers to these questions first. Keep track of your time.

1. The polar bear, whose habitat is the Arctic region, is known by many other names. List at least two here. _____

   _____

2. What is between Earth's mantle and its atmosphere? _____

   _____

3. Where is the largest cold desert in the world? _____

   _____

4. Name two land features that are formed by melting glaciers. _____

   _____

   _____

5. What can be affected by latitude, altitude and distance from a large body of water?

   _____

6. Where are currents found? _____

   _____

7. List two forms of precipitation. _____

   _____

8. What did Benjamin Franklin observe that affected weather? _____

   _____

   _____

9. What other word shares the word part *equ* with the word *equinox*? How are both words

   similar? _____

   _____

10. When did the Greek philosopher Pythagoras live? _____

    _____

Name .... Date ....

Rock testing

Practise working with rocks. Collect several rocks and see what you can discover.

Directions: Observe and experiment on the rocks you collected. Then complete the chart.

	Appearance Describe your rock.	**Scratch test** Can you scratch it with a nail? A coin? A fingernail?	**Source** Where did you get your rock from?	**Type** Is your rock sedimentary, igneous or metamorphic?
1.				
2.				
3.				
4.				
5.				
6.				

Name .... Date ....

Prior knowledge

You probably already know more about the universe than you realise. Do this activity before you read *Factoscope: Universe* to find out what you do—and don't—already know.

Directions: Put a tick next to the words you know have to do with space, features of space or the study of space. Circle words that are unfamiliar to you or that do not seem to have anything to do with the study of space. Look for these words as you read the book.

terrestrial	composition
intergalactic	gravitation
mass	neutron
constituents	luminosity
ellipses	diffuse
revolution	rotation

Word parts

The word *protostar* means 'first form of a star', while the word *protogalaxy* means 'first form of a galaxy'. The word part *proto* means 'first form'.

Directions: Study each pair of words and their definitions. Then underline the word part they have in common and write your own definition of the word part.

1. **geocentric** *(ge/o/cen/tric)*: centred around the Earth

   heliocentric *(hel/i/o/cen/tric)*: centred around the sun

   _____

   _____

2. **atmosphere** *(at/mo/sphere)*: the air surrounding a planet

   chromosphere *(chro/mo/sphere)*: bright or colourful gaseous layer around the sun

   _____

   _____

3. **geosynchronous** *(ge/o/synch/ron/ous)*: moving at the same pace as Earth

   sun-synchronous *(sun/syn/chron/ous)*: crossing a given spot at the same local solar time

   _____

   _____

Name .... Date ....

Word relationships

The vocabulary of the English language is related to that of many other languages. English has borrowed words and word parts from Greek, Latin, Italian, French, Japanese and many others.

```
             ┌──────────• astronaut •──────────┐
             │                                 │
 astro = star (from Greek)        naut = sailor (from French)
```

Related words: astronomy, astrology, asterisk, nautical, navy, nautilus

Directions: Find each word or phrase in the book *Factoscope: Universe*. Explain each term and discuss its origin. List other English words that are related.

1. Carte du Ciel *(see page 20)*

   _____

   _____

2. Stella Polaris *(see page 21)*

   _____

   _____

3. Ursa Major *(see page 24)*

   _____

   _____

4. sol *(see page 28)*

   _____

   _____

5. Titan *(see page 40)*

   _____

   _____

6. meteor *(see page 45)*

   _____

Name .... Date ....

List-group-label

What do these words have in common?

visual binaries   **optical doubles**   **barycentre**

They are all words to do with binary star systems.

Directions: Group related words from the box below. You may use the same word in more than one group or add words of your own. Label each group.

asterism	eclipsing	intrinsic	rotate
astronaut	explosive	nebulae	supernovae
celestial	extrinsic	protestars	taikonaut
constellation	gases	pulsating	terrestrial
cosmonaut	intergalactic	revolve	zodiac

Name .... Date ....

Who?

Directions: Find each person listed below in the book *Factoscope: Universe.* Write a paragraph about that person, telling when he lived and what he contributed to our understanding of the universe.

1. Sir William Herschel

_____

_____

_____

2. Edwin Powell Hubble

_____

_____

_____

3. Abd al-Rahman al-Sufi

_____

_____

_____

_____

4. Galileo Galilei

_____

_____

_____

_____

5. Yuri Gagarin

_____

_____

_____

Name .... Date ....

Time line

Directions: Put the events listed below and the people from the previous activity in chronological order to create a time line. Space the elements of your time line in a logical way and write a title for it.

- European navigators drew and named constellations to help them find their way.
- Babylonians made the first known star chart.
- An Indian scholar accurately explained eclipses.
- Halley's comet is last seen from Earth in 1986.
- Early astronomers built Stonehenge in what is now England.
- Chinese astronomers charted comets.

Name .... Date ....

Universal numbers

Mercury goes around the sun in 88 days, or about four times in one Earth year. How do we know?

88 days = Mercury's revolution around the sun (Mercury's year)

365 days = Earth's revolution around the sun (Earth's year)

365 days ÷ 88 days = 4.15

Directions: Answer the questions comparing days and years in our solar system. Find the numbers you need in *Factoscope: Universe*.

1. How long does it take in Earth years for Neptune to orbit the sun?

   _____

2. How long is Neptune's day compared to Earth's?

   _____

3. How do Venus's year and day compare?

   _____

4. Which planet's day is about the same length as Earth's?

   _____

5. How long is a Martian year?

   _____

6. How long is Saturn's day compared to Earth's?

   _____

7. Look at the lengths of days on the planets. Which has the shortest day? Which has the longest?

   _____

8. What generalisation can you make about the length of a year on the planets in our solar system? (Hint: Look for a pattern related to the distance of each planet from the sun.)

   _____

   _____

   _____

Name .... Date ....

Venn diagram

Look at the pairs of terms below. Think about how they compare and contrast.

meteors and meteorites   **Galileo and Hubble**   **any two planets**

asteroids and planets   **shooting stars and auroras**

Directions: Circle one of the pairs above. Create a Venn diagram to compare and contrast them. Write the facts that are different about each term in its own oval. Write the facts that are similar in the area that the two ovals share.

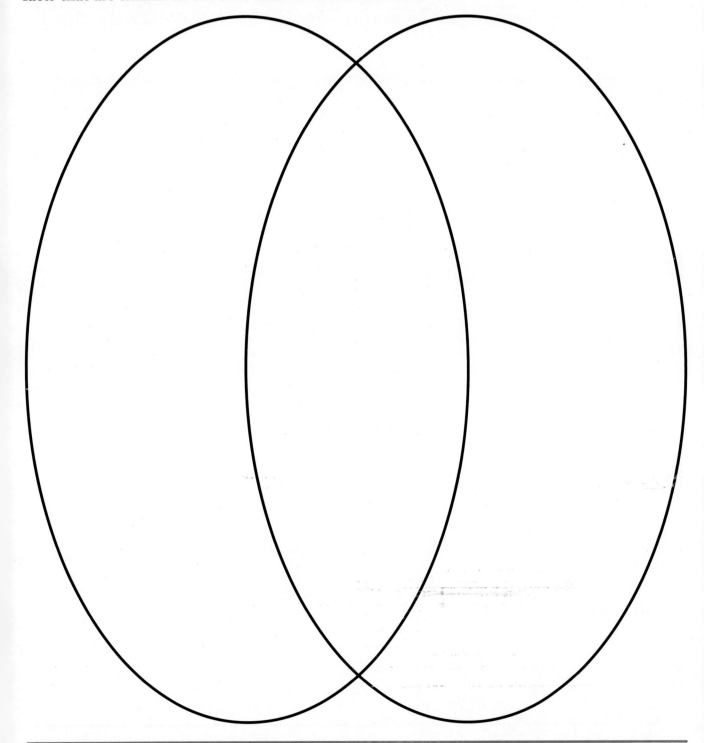

Name .... Date ....

Choose a project

Directions: Read the following options. Choose a project to complete on your own. Use the space below to list the resources you will use.

- Research and write a 'how to' guide on telling the difference between stars and planets in the night sky.

- Draw a diagram on the progression of an eclipse (solar or lunar) and complete with labels and/or explanations.

- Write a short biography on an astronomer or team of astronomers and his/her/their discoveries.

- Illustrate the life cycle of a star. (Hint: You might use a branching or tree diagram.)

- Draw a star chart of the constellations you can see from your own garden this month.

PROJECT
RESOURCE
Factoscope: Universe pages:
Books:
Websites:
Other resources

Name _____ Date _____

Scavenger hunt

Use the index of *Factoscope: Universe* and a stopwatch to test your hunting skills.

Directions: Go it alone or team up with a partner and compete against another pair to see who can find the answers to these questions first. Keep track of your time.

1. What kind of celestial body is a coma part of? _____

    _____

2. What type of star is Algol? Name a star of a different type. _____

    _____

3. The word *umbra* means 'shadow' and the word part *pen* means 'almost'. Explain how the word *penumbra* is used both with sunspots and eclipses.

    _____

4. What is unusual about Saturn's largest moon, Titan? _____

5. List at least three other names for the Pole Star. _____

    _____

6. The word *mons* is related to 'mountain'. Where is the largest mountain in our solar system and what is it called?

    _____

7. Many ancient civilisations made up stories to explain astronomical events. List at least three different groups that created their own myths or legends for this purpose.

    _____

    _____

8. Name two astronomical events that early cultures used to create myths about to explain them.

    _____

9. What is the difference between a planetarium and an observatory?

    _____

10. What did Galileo have to do with the telescope? _____

    _____

Name .... Date ....

Meanings of prefixes

In the word *antibody*, the prefix *anti* means 'against'.

antibody: a protein to fight against foreign bodies, such as germs and viruses

Directions: Study each set of words and their definitions. Then underline the word part they have in common and write your own definition of the word part.

1. **internal** *(in/ter/nal)* – located within

   intercostal *(in/ter/cost/al)* – between the ribs

   _____

   _____

2. **transmit** *(trans/mit)* – to pass along

   transplant *(trans/plant)* – to move something from one place to another

   _____

   _____

3. **exhale** *(ex/hale)* – breathe out

   extend *(ex/tend)* – to stretch out

   excrete *(ex/crete)* – to eliminate from the body as waste

   _____

   _____

4. **undigested** *(un/di/gest/ed)* – not absorbed by the body

   uncontrolled *(un/con/trolled)* – not limited

   _____

   _____

Search and find

Directions: List other words from the book that have the same prefixes you underlined above. Add other words you know that also fit.

_____

_____

_____

_____

Name .... Date ....

Forming plurals

One branch of the windpipe is a *bronchus*, while the two together are called *bronchi*. What other interesting plurals can you find in the science of biology?

Directions: Look at the words in the box and list each under the heading that describes how to change the singular form of the word into the plural form. Write the plural form of the word next to it.

alveolus	artery	body
deficiency	disease	mosquito
muscle	radius	surgery
therapy	tissue	tooth
toe	villus	woman

Add *-s*	Add *-es*

Change *-y* to *-ies*	Irregular plurals

Name .... Date ....

List-group-label

What do these words have in common?

> **epithelium**   **muscular**   **nervous**   **connective**

They are the four types of tissue in the human body.

Directions: Group related words from the box below. You may use the same word in more than one group or add words of your own. Label each group.

arteries	diabetes	liver	asthma	endocrine glands
nose	brain	gall bladder	pituitary	cancer
heart	sinusoids	capillaries	intestines	skin
chickenpox	kidneys	smallbox	veins	yellow fever

Name .... Date ....

It runs in the family

Who do you most look like in your family? Where do your traits come from? Do this project to explore the topic.

Directions: Fill in the chart about yourself. Then choose two other family members that you can observe and complete the chart about each of them.

Family member: Yourself

☐ Free earlobes	☐ Attached earlobes	☐ Hair on fingers
☐ No hair on fingers	☐ Widow's peak	☐ No widow's peak
☐ Curly hair	☐ Straight hair	☐ Can't curl tongue
☐ Can curl tongue	☐ Cleft chin	☐ Smooth chin
☐ Smile dimples	☐ No smile dimples	

Family member: _____

☐ Free earlobes	☐ Attached earlobes	☐ Hair on fingers
☐ No hair on fingers	☐ Widow's peak	☐ No widow's peak
☐ Curly hair	☐ Straight hair	☐ Can't curl tongue
☐ Can curl tongue	☐ Cleft chin	☐ Smooth chin
☐ Smile dimples	☐ No smile dimples	

Family member: _____

☐ Free earlobes	☐ Attached earlobes	☐ Hair on fingers
☐ No hair on fingers	☐ Widow's peak	☐ No widow's peak
☐ Curly hair	☐ Straight hair	☐ Can't curl tongue
☐ Can curl tongue	☐ Cleft chin	☐ Smooth chin
☐ Smile dimples	☐ No smile dimples	

Name _____ Date _____

How many heartbeats?

How many times does your heart beat per minute? How many times should it beat? This project will help you find out.

Directions: Follow the instructions to complete this page about your heart after you have been sitting quietly for awhile.

1. Find a pulse point on your wrist or one side of your neck using your finger (not your thumb). Using a clock with a second hand, count the number of times you feel your heartbeat during a 10 second period. Multiply that number by six.

   Record your heart rate here: _____

2. People between the ages of eight and 15 should have a resting heart rate somewhere between 70–100, the average being 84 beats a minute. The average adult's heart rate is slightly lower. How does your heart rate compare to the average person your age?

   _____

   _____

   _____

3. Stand up and sit down three times in a row, then take your heart rate in the same way you did before.

   Record your heart rate here: _____

4. Now do some moderate exercise for 20 to 30 minutes. Take your heart rate in the same way you did before.

   Record your heart rate here: _____

5. Rest for three to five minutes, then take your heart rate in the same way you did before.

   Record your heart rate here: _____

6. When did your heart pump fastest? Why do you think your heart beat rate changed?

   _____

   _____

   _____

Name .... Date ....

Venn diagram

Look at the pairs of terms below. Think about how they compare and contrast.

digestion and breathing   **nose and ears**   **clones and babies**

transfusions and dialysis   **circulatory system and respiratory system**

Directions: Circle one of the pairs above. Create a Venn diagram to compare and contrast them. Write the facts that are different about each term in its own oval. Write the facts that are similar in the area that the two ovals share.

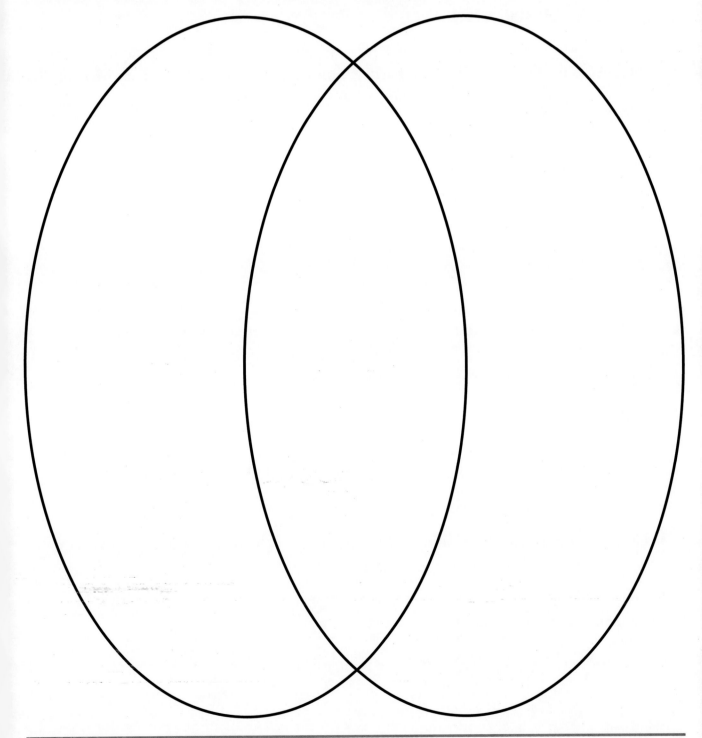

Name .... Date ....

Choose a project

Directions: Read the following options. Choose one project to complete on your own.

Project 1: Body system map

Draw a diagram of one of the systems of the body, explaining the system's processes from start to finish. Be sure to use labels. Systems to consider include: circulatory, nervous, respiratory, digestive or another of your choosing.

Project 2: Mendel's trait wheel

The 'It runs in the family' project on page 43 gave you a glimpse at the different dominant and recessive traits that a person can inherit. A famous genetic scientist, Gregor Mendel, created a 'trait wheel' showing these different features. There are 134 combinations in all. Use the library or the Internet to find Mendel's trait wheel. Determine where you fit on the wheel. What traits do you have? Which are dominant and which are recessive? From whom did you inherit these traits? You may wish to record the information you gather in charts similar to those on page 43.

Project 3: Chickenpox survey

Because smaller children seem less affected by the highly contagious disease known as chickenpox, many parents purposely expose their children to it when given a chance. Survey everyone you know to see who has had the illness and at what age they contracted it. Ask those who had the disease as children if they were exposed to it on purpose. Compile the information as a table or chart and report your findings to the class.

Project 4: Research

Research and write a one-page essay on one of the following topics:

- **Vaccinations:** How they actually work and how they have helped people live longer.

- **Controversial medicine:** Cloning and stem cell research are both hot topics. What is your educated opinion about these issues?

- **'The father of dialysis'**, Thomas Graham, was a chemist, not a doctor, and yet he developed the first dialysis machine. Explain how.

Name .... Date ....

Scavenger hunt

Use the index of *Factoscope: Human body* and a stopwatch to test your hunting skills.

Directions: Go it alone or team up with a partner and compete against another pair to see who can find the answers to these questions first. Keep track of your time.

1. Where is your parotid gland? _____
   _____

2. What does the human body produce to counteract antigens? _____
   _____

3. Name three parts of the body the pituitary gland regulates. _____
   _____

4. While the word 'axial' has to do with parts of the body from head to waist, what is the word having to do with the limbs?
   _____

5. What do nucleotides pair together to form? _____
   _____

6. What is a synonym for the word trachea? _____
   _____

7. What is the cardiac cycle? _____
   _____
   _____

8. Who was the first person to experiment with genetics? _____
   _____

9. List at least three specific parts of the lymphatic system. _____
   _____

10. What does the endocrine system do? Give an example of what it does for the body.
   _____
   _____

Name .... Date ....

Cloze

Directions: Choose a word from the box to fill in each blank to have the paragraph make sense. Hint: Not all words will be used.

AIDS	**infectious**
allergens	**infected**
chickenpox	**mumps**
curable	**preventable**
diseases	**vaccines**
incubation	**viral**
viruses	**defences**

The human body is a wondrous thing—especially when all its parts are working.

Sometimes, however, something goes wrong, such as when it is attacked by a

_____ infection. To be cured, usually the _____ person takes

medicine. However, for some diseases, such as _____, the sick person simply

has to wait out the infection. Many _____, including yellow fever and

_____, are now only limited to certain parts of the world. That is because

many people get 'shots', or _____, to protect themselves against these

_____ . These diseases are said to be _____. Sadly, in some

countries the vaccinations are too costly or simply not yet available.

Name .... Date ....

Word parts

The word *rechargeable* comes from the word parts *re* (meaning 'again'), *charge* (meaning 'to supply with electrical energy') and *able* (meaning 'capable of'). In other words, a rechargeable battery can be supplied again with energy and used several times.

Directions: Combine the word parts in the box to create words from the book. Apply the explanations of the word parts to write your own definition for each word. Use the book or a dictionary if needed. You can use each word part more than once.

---

baro – weight or pressure
graph – writing
metre/meter – unit of measurement, measuring device
scope – instrument for observing
stetho – chest
tele – distant, transmission over distance
thermo – temperature or heat

_____

_____

_____

_____

_____

Related words

Many of the word parts you used in the activity above appear in other words you know.

The words *thermometer*, *thermal* and *thermos* are related because they all contain the word part that means heat or temperature.

Directions: List other words you know that use word parts from the box above.

_____

_____

_____

_____

Name .... Date ....

Thinking skills: Categories

What do these words have in common?

Archimedes   **Thomas Edison**   **Elisha Otis**

Directions: Write a category label for each group of words or names. Then add another word or names to each group.

1. Label: _____

   battery   *internal-combustion engine*   *dynamo*   _____

2. Label: _____

   radio   *telephone*   *telegraph*   _____

3. Label:_____

   light bulb   *movie camera*   *electric light*   _____

4. Label: _____

   rickshaw   *bicycle*   *steam engine*   _____

5. Label: _____

   catapult   *revolver*   *guided missile*   _____

Thinking skills: Logic

All machines are inventions, but not all inventions are machines.

Directions: Explain this statement in your own words.

_____

_____

_____

_____

_____

_____

_____

Name .... Date ....

Comprehension: True or false?

Before you read: Read the statements and decide whether they are true or false.
As you read *Factoscope: Machines and inventions*, keep an eye out for facts that prove the
statements as true or false.

1. The idea for the wheel started as rollers. .... T   F
2. Water was drawn from wells by a machine that works much like a seesaw. .... T   F
3. Using pulleys correctly, one person can lift a full ship by him/herself. .... T   F
4. Isaac Singer invented the sewing device. .... T   F
5. The first bicycles did not have pedals or rubber tyres. .... T   F
6. Egyptians created the first kind of paper. .... T   F
7. A barometer is used for weighing things. .... T   F
8. Thomas Edison invented the very first light bulb. .... T   F
9. The first building to be called a skyscraper was only nine storeys tall. .... T   F
10. An American, Henry Ford, invented the first automobile. .... T   F

After you read: Use information in the book to correct your answers above. Choose
one true statement from above and write examples from the book that prove it. Then
choose a false statement from above and write examples that disprove it.

True statement: _____

_____

_____

_____

_____

_____

False statement: _____

_____

_____

_____

_____

_____

Name .... Date ....

Top ten

Factoscope: Machines and inventions discusses many important inventions. In your opinion, which are the most important? Was anything left out of the book?

Directions: Write your own top ten list of the most important inventions in history. Include inventions from the book or add others you know. Fill in other important details as specified by the chart below.

	Invention	Inventor(s)	Date	Importance
10.				
9.				
8.				
7.				
6.				
5.				
4.				
3.				
2.				
1.				

Invention time line

wheel ⟶ cart ⟶ chariot ⟶ carriage ⟶ automobile

Directions: Create your own invention time line with a series of inventions that are related. Use arrows to show the order in which they were created.

Name .... Date ....

Simple machines

Simple machines are tools that make work easier.

Directions: Draw an example of the simple machine under its definition.

1. **lever** – a board or bar that rests on a turning point (called a fulcrum). Whatever a lever moves is called its 'load'.	2. **wheel and axle** – The axle is a rod that goes through the wheel. It helps the wheel turn.
3. **inclined plane** – A smooth surface that is angled so that one end is higher than the other.	4. **screw** – A screw is an inclined plane that winds around itself. It can raise or lower things, or hold things together.
5. **wedge** – Two inclined planes placed together form a sharp edge that can split objects apart.	6. **pulley** – A pulley is a grooved wheel with rope that fits on the wheel. One end of the rope is attached to a load, the other to the energy source, be it human, animal or mechanical.

Name .... Date ....

Experiment with simple machines

Directions: Follow the directions, then answer the questions.

Experiment #1   Put a light book close to the edge of a desk or table. Place a wooden ruler halfway under it and halfway off the desk. Raise the book by pressing down on the ruler. Move the book by pulling on the ruler. Continue until the book is at the edge of the table. Try again with a shorter/longer ruler.

1. What kind of simple machine did you make? _____

2. Was it easier to lift the book with a short or long ruler? _____

Experiment #2   Put a pencil through the middle of a plastic cotton spool. Have one person hold the pencil (not the spool). Wrap a piece of string once around the spool, then tie a knot in the middle of the string. Have someone pull one end of the string to see how the knot moves. Next, put another pencil through another spool and have another person hold the pencil. Loop the string around the second spool so that the one loop goes around both spools. Tie the ends of the string together. Have a third person pull the string to move the knot back and forth.

3. What kind of simple machine did you make? _____

4. How did you change the direction of the knot? _____

5. How could you add weight (load) to your experiment? How much weight do you think your string could lift or carry?

_____

Experiment #3   Collect several different screw-top jars with lids. Each line that goes around the inside of the lid is a thread. Predict how many threads the average lid has and write it below. Mark a place on the lid with a marker or a piece of tape. As you unscrew the lid, count it as one turn each time you see your mark.

6. How many threads do you predict the average jar lid has? _____

7. How many threads does the average jar lid have? (Add each total, then divide by of jars for your average.)

_____

Name .... Date ....

Imagine an interview

What would Ts'ai Lun, the inventor of paper, think of our books, mail and magazines today? Would he think our paper is much different from his invention?

Directions: Write answers to the interviewer's questions as if you were Ts'ai Lun.

Interviewer: So what made you think of mixing different plants together to make paper?

Ts'ai Lun: _____

_____

Interviewer: Clever! Well, what do you think of how we use paper today? Do you think we've made any improvements to your design?

Ts'ai Lun: _____

_____

Interviewer: Is there anything we're doing with paper today that you would change?

Ts'ai Lun: _____

_____

Interviewer: With the relatively new invention of the computer, we're moving into a 'paperless' age, where we are reading our news and books online and keeping our records without using paper. Do you think this is good thing?

Ts'ai Lun: _____

_____

Make your own paper

This recipe doesn't use plants as a main ingredient, but recycled paper. So collect any unwanted clean paper and start creating ...

1. Cut the paper into strips, then soak it overnight in a bucket of water with two tablespoons of bleach and two tablespoons of baking soda (to soften and whiten the paper).

2. The next morning, you may wish to boil the paper to further soften it. Then put the paper and water in a food processor or blender.

3. Add dye (liquid or powder), mix, then drain any extra liquid. Add a little cornflour.

4. Place wax paper on an ironing board, then place the mixture on the wax paper and shape it as desired. If you would like, add dried grass, leaves or flowers. Layer another sheet of wax paper on top, then use an iron to flatten and dry the mixture. It will take a while to completely dry. Laying it flat in the sun may help.

Name _____ Date _____

Your own invention

What do you think needs to be invented or improved? Here's your chance to be an inventor yourself!

Directions: Think of something that you've seen a need for. What would it take to make it? Plan it out and fill out the patent application so that no one else can steal your design idea.

I, (**name**) _____, have invented a new design for

a (**invention**) _____, which

(**explanation**) _____

_____

_____

as set forth in the following specification:

(Figure 1) _____ is a view thereof.

(Figure 2) _____ is a view thereof.

I claim the ornamental design for a _____ as shown below (logo).

_____ **Patent and Trademark Office**
(Write the adjectival name of your country)

An Agency of the Intellectual Property Department of _____
(Your country)

Name .... Date ....

Scavenger hunt

Use the index of *Factoscope: Machines and inventions* and stopwatch to test your hunting skills.

Directions: Go it alone or team up with a partner and compete against another pair to see who can find the answers to these questions first. Keep track of your time.

1. What was the nickname for Thomas Edison's main continuous-current dynamo?

   _____

2. What simple machine, beside a wheel and axle, uses an axle?

   _____

3. What product did the Raytheon Company create?

   _____

4. When was a full keyboard first used?

   _____

5. What or who started the Second Industrial Revolution?

   _____

6. Who invented the form of transportation known as the rickshaw?

   _____

7. What did Alessandro Volta invent?

   _____

8. What did Galileo Galilei invent?

   _____

   _____

9. How did Bertha Benz help with the invention of the car?

   _____

   _____

10. What does the word *hydraulic* mean? _____

   _____

Answers

Answer key for *Plants*

Word parts .... p. 4

Possible words:

antifungal – against fungus; autotroph – a plant that makes its own food; carbohydrate – energy in the form of carbon and water; lithophyte – a plant that grows on stone; hydrophyte – a plant that grows in extremely wet places

Related words .... p. 4

Possible words: automobile, automatic, hydroplane, hydrant, hydrogen, lithosphere, monolith, xerophyte, epiphyte, halophyte, sporophyte

Label groups .... p. 5

Sample responses: 1. What plants need to survive, carbohydrates or chlorophyll; 2. Palm trees, coconut; 3. Forest types, tropical rainforest; 4. How seeds are spread, water; 5. Plant parts, flower; 6. Plant defences, prickers

Do-it-yourself groupings .... p. 5

Answers will vary.

Create a diagram .... p. 6

Answers will vary.

Grow-your-own experiment .... p. 7

Answers will vary.

Plant condition chart .... p. 8

Answers will vary.

Everyday inventory .... p. 9

Answers will vary.

Garden classification .... p. 10

Answers will vary.

Scavenger hunt .... p. 11

1. primary
2. seed-like objects involved with reproduction
3. rocks, streams, trees, forest floors, mountain tops
4. yearly or annual
5. trees, exotic plants and outdoor plants
6. thalloid
7. in warm, damp areas (in the same places you'd find palms and ferns)
8. chlorophyll, chloroplasts
9. Monocots have flowers set in groups of three or multiples of three, while dicots have flowers set in groups of fours or fives.
10. sago palm

Cloze .... p. 12

Words in order:
varieties
chlorophyll
leaves
palo verde
photosynthesis
reproduce
endangered

Answer key for *Animal world*

Write definitions .... p. 13

Sample responses: 1. a sense of timing within an animal that helps it know general time of day or season without being told; 2. is awake during the night-time; 3. already dead animals; 4. lives in trees; 5. poisonous; 6. live in

Like and unlike .... p. 14

Sample responses: 1. c – When animals migrate, they travel back and forth to places depending on the season.; 2. e – Some animals hibernate in the cold, other animals estivate in the heat.; 3. b – An exoskeleton may be in the form of a shell, or a hard outer covering.; 4. a – The poles are in the Arctic and in Antarctica.; 5. d – Species is a more specific way to group animals; genus is more general.

Synonym or antonym .... p. 14

1. S
2. S
3. A
4. A
5. S
6. A

Venn diagram .... p. 15

Answers will vary.

Classifications .... p. 16

1. invertebrate, cold-blooded, venomous, aquatic
2. mammal, vertebrate, oviparous (egg-laying), semiaquatic, venomous, carnivore, endothermic
3. insect, invertebrate, herbivore, nectivore, pollinator, oviparous, cold-blooded
4. mammal, vertebrate, carnivore, fissiped, land animals, viviparous, hibernators, warm-blooded
5. vertebrate, bird, semiaquatic, oviparous, flightless bird, polar, warm-blooded, carnivore
6. mammal, vertebrate, rodent, hibernator, viviparous, herbivore, arboreal, warm-blooded
7. Answers will vary.
8. Answers will vary.

Answers

Your local habitat..........................**p. 17**

Answers will vary.

Habitat observations........................**p. 18**

Answers will vary.

Choose a project.............................**p. 19**

Answers will vary.

Scavenger hunt...............................**p. 20**

1. bat
2. They both eat carrion (dead meat).
3. polar bear
4. They can both change their skin colour.
5. penguins, walruses
6. It lives in or near fresh water.
7. Possible responses include bats, dolphins, butterflies, tree frogs, birds, fish, lemurs.
8. ungulate
9. Possible responses include: shiver, migrate, crowd together, move their wings to generate heat.
10. orangutans

Cloze..**p. 21**

Words in order:
characteristics
grow
breathe
oxygen
habitat
invertebrates
spine
worms

Answer key for *Earth*

Prior knowledge..............................**p. 22**

Answers will vary.

Word parts.....................................**p. 22**

Sample answers:
1. underline photo - light
2. underline ex - out
3. underline semi - partly

Word scramble................................**p. 23**

1. earthquake
2. precipitation
3. substratum
4. longitudes
5. climate
6. tsunami
7. eruption

8. sedimentary
9. continental drift
10. metamorphic

Cause and effect.............................**p. 24**

1. Cause: tectonic plates move, Effect: earthquake
2. Cause: earthquake, Effect: tsunami
3. Cause: Earth rotates relative to the sun, Effect: Time of day varies around the globe
4. Cause: water condenses in the clouds, Effect: precipitation falls in some form
5. Cause: tsunami, Effect: flood
6. Cause: rivers flow, Effect: vallyes form
7. Cause: hot lava cools, Effect: igneous rock forms

Explain...**p. 24**

Answers will vary.

Create a diagram.............................**p. 25**

Answers will vary.

Local features project.......................**p. 26**

Answers will vary.

Natural wonders..............................**p. 27**

No response required.

Map the Seven Wonders.....................**p. 28**

Map should show:
Grand Canyon in the south-western United States
The Great Barrier Reef off the north-east coast of Australia
Aurora borealis in the northern polar region
Victoria Falls between Zambia and Zimbabwe
Paricutin in Mexico
Mt Everest in Asia between Nepal and Tibet
The harbour at Rio de Janeiro on the coast of Brazil

Your thoughts.................................**p. 28**

Answers will vary.

Scavenger hunt...............................**p. 29**

1. white bear, northern bear, sea bear
2. the crust
3. Antarctica
4. cirque or cave
5. an area's climate
6. oceans, rivers, atmosphere (air currents)
7. Answers will vary: rain, snow, sleet, hail
8. volcanic eruptions
9. equator; Both words are about partitioning something in half.
10. 6th century BCE

Answers

Rock testing .... p. 30

Pupils' responses will depend on the rock specimens they have chosen.

Answer key for *Universe*

Prior knowledge .... p. 31

Answers will vary.

Word parts .... p. 31

Sample answers:
1. underline *centric* – centred around one point
2. underline *sphere* – round object
3. underline *synchronous* – at the same time

Word relationships .... p. 32

1. *Carte du Ciel* means 'map the sky'. Astronomers wanted to map what the night sky looked like. *ciel* looks like *ceiling* and *celestial*; *carte* is like *chart*;
2. Polaris means *pole*; *stella* means *star*. *Stella Polaris* refers to the star above the North Pole. Other words: *polar*, *stellar*;
3. *Major* means *great*, so *Ursa* must mean *bear*. The constellation looks a little like a big bear.;
4. *Sol* was the Latin word for *sun*. Other words: *solar*, *solstice*;
5. Titan is a large moon of Saturn. Another word is *titanic*.;
6. Meteors are commonly known as *falling stars*. Other words: *meteoroids*, *meteorites*.

List-group-label .... p. 33

Answers will vary. Possible responses:

Terms for space explorers: astronauts, cosmonauts, taikonauts; Variable stars: extrinsic, intrinsic, eclipsing, pulsating, explosive; Words with unconventional plurals: supernovae, nebulae, gases; Sky signposts: constellations: asterisms, zodiac

Who? .... p. 34

Dates are approximate:
1. Herschel lived in the early 1800s. He discovered planets, studied stars and recorded other heavenly bodies.
2. Hubble worked in the early to mid 1900s. He was a famous astronomer.
3. Abd al-Rahman al-Sufi lived in the 900s. He was the first person to record an observation of the Andromeda galaxy.
4. Galileo Galilei lived in the 16th and 17th centuries. He invented a better telescope and helped prove that the Earth is not the center of the universe.
5. In the 1960s, Gagarin was the first human in outer space.

Time line .... p. 35

Order should be as follows:
- Early astronomers built Stonehenge in what is now England.
- Chinese astronomers charted comets.
- Persian astronomer, Abd al-Rahman al-Sufi, saw Andromeda.
- Babylonians made the first known star chart.
- An Indian scholar accurately explained eclipses.
- European navigators drew and named constellations to help find their way.
- Galileo Galilei improved the telescope and astronomy forever.
- Sir Herschel discovered stars and planets.
- Hubble made many important modern-day discoveries.
- Yuri Gagarin was the first person in outer space.
- Halley's comet is last seen here on Earth in 1986.

Universal numbers .... p. 36

1. 165 years
2. About $^2/_3$ the time of an Earth day.
3. They are almost the same—its day is actually a little longer than its year.
4. Mars
5. Almost 2 Earth years
6. About 40% shorter
7. Venus has the longest day and Jupiter has the shortest day
8. Planets in our system that are further from the Sun have a longer year because they take longer to orbit the Sun.

Venn diagram .... p. 37

Answers will vary.

Choose a project .... p. 38

Answers will vary.

Scavenger hunt .... p. 39

1. a comet;
2. binary star, our sun;
3. Both have very dark parts and less dark parts.
4. Titan is a satellite that has an atmosphere.;
5. North pole star, Polaris, Tou Mu, Polaris Kynosoura, Stella Polaris, Lodestar, Steering Star, Ship Star, or Stella Maris;
6. Olympus Mons is on Mars.
7. Hindus, Chinese, Greeks, Romans, Chaldeans
8. eclipses, constellations;
9. A planetarium is a theatre that shows models of the night sky. An observatory has actual telescopes and other instruments for observing the sky.
10. He didn't invent it, but he improved it.

Answers

Meanings of prefixes .... p. 40

Sample responses:

1. underline inter - between or within
2. underline trans - across
3. underline ex - out
4. underline un - not

Search and find .... p. 40

Possible responses:
international, intercellular, intersegmental, interprets, interior
transfusion, transportation, transfer, transparent, transmission
expansion, expiration
unprotected, unscreened

Forming plurals .... p. 41

Add *-s* or *-es*: diseases-diseases, muscle-muscles, tissue-
tissues, toe-toes

Add *-es*: mosquito-mosquitoes

Change *-y* to *-ies*: artery-arteries, body-bodies, deficiency-
deficiencies, surgery-surgeries, therapy-therapies

Irregular plurals: alveolus-alveoli, radius-radii, tooth-teeth,
villus-villi, woman-women

List-group-label .... p. 42

Possible responses:

Types of blood vessels: arteries, veins, capillaries, sinusoids

Organs: skin, liver, nose, gall bladder, kidneys, brain,
intestines, heart

Diseases: asthma, diabetes, cancer, yellow fever, chickenpox,
smallpox

It runs in the family .... p. 43

Answers will vary.

How many heartbeats? .... p. 44

Answers will vary.

Venn diagram .... p. 45

Answers will vary.

Choose a project .... p. 46

Answers will vary.

Scavenger hunt .... p. 47

1. neck
2. antibodies

3. hormones, bones and tissue
4. appendicular
5. the chemical bases for DNA
6. windpipe
7. the pumping of the heart
8. Gregor Mendel
9. lymph vessels, lymph nodes, antibodies, chyle and
   lymphatic organs
10. makes hormones, which regulates activities like sleep and
    hunger

Cloze .... p. 48

Words in order:
viral
infected
chickenpox
diseases or viruses
mumps
vaccines
viruses or diseases
preventable

Word parts .... p. 49

Definitions may vary. Sample answers:

barometer – an instrument that measures air pressure, it helps
predict the weather

telegraph – a device used to send messages over long distances

telescope – an instrument used to see faraway objects

stethoscope – a device for examining the chest area

thermometer – an instrument for measuring one's temperature

Related words .... p. 49

Sample answers: television, microscope, anemometer,
diameter, millimetre, arithmometer, photographic, radiograph,
tomography, lithography, anemoscope, autograph, biography,
graphic

Thinking skills: Categories .... p. 50

1. Power sources, turbine
2. Ways to communicate over distances, fibre optics
3. Patents held by Thomas Edison, electric railways
4. Types of transportation, automobile
5. Weapons, trebuchet

Thinking skills: Logic .... p. 50

Sample answer: All machines are things that are made to help
people do work of some kind. But some inventions are not
things, but ideas such as new kinds of music or a new scientific
theory.

Answers

Comprehension: True or false? .... p. 51

1. T	2. T
3. T	4. F
5. T	6. F
7. F	8. F
9. T	10. F

Sample answer: True: The first bicycle had wooden tyres. It was invented in 1790. The first pedal-driven bike was created in 1839. False: A French engineer invented the first automobile in 1769. Henry Ford built his automobile in 1886.

Top ten .... p. 52

Answers will vary.

Invention time line .... p. 52

Answers will vary.

Simple machines .... p. 53

Pupils' drawings will vary.

Experiment with simple machines .... p. 54

1. lever
2. long should be easier
3. pulley
4. added another pulley
5. Answers will vary.
6. Answers will vary.
7. Answers will vary.

Imagine an interview .... p. 55

Answers will vary.

Make your own paper .... p. 55

Pupils' work will vary.

Your own invention .... p. 56

Answers will vary.

Scavenger hunt .... p. 57

1. long-legged Mary-Ann
2. pulley
3. microwave ovens
4. 1888
5. Niokla Tesla's motors
6. Jonathan Scobie
7. the battery
8. thermometer
9. She drove her husband's invention 106 kilometres.
10. *Hydraulic* has to do with water.